Baby Animals

kitten trail

Which path leads the kitten to the bowl of milk?

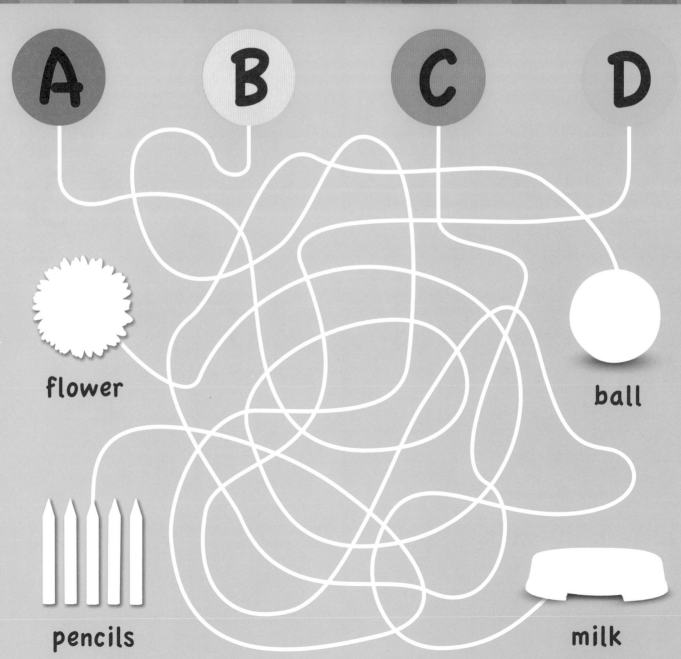

A   B   C   D

flower

ball

pencils

milk

Baby jigsaw

Find the missing jigsaw pieces to complete your favorite baby animals.

baboon

chicks

seal pup

elephant calf

Match & color

Find the sticker then color in the drawing to match.

three kittens

Word search

Find the missing stickers then circle the hidden words in the box.

puppy   piglet   calf   lion cub   kitten

a	m	o	e	f	g	i	a	l	a	l	k
c	a	l	f	i	a	c	d	u	i
l	e	m	c	p	i	g	l	e	t
k	i	x	h	u	t	b	n	r	t
o	h	u	z	p	o	g	a	i	e
b	w	a	r	p	n	u	y	a	n
f	t	e	r	y	a	h	m	l	o
d	a	l	i	o	n	c	u	b	x

Baby patterns

Find the missing stickers to complete the patterns.

What's different?

Circle five differences between these two pictures.

counting animals

Can you count from 1 to 10? Write the number and find the missing stickers.

1 one caterpillar

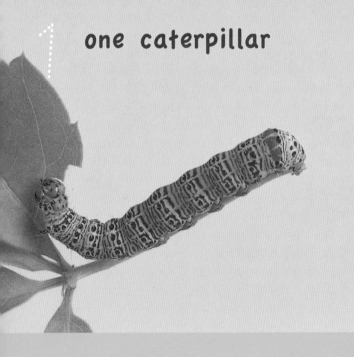

2 two kittens

3 three owl chicks

4 four giraffe foals

5 five donkey foals

6 six boar piglets

7 seven deer fawns

8 eight ostrich chicks

9 nine lambs

10 ten puppies

Babies at play

Baby animals love to play. Can you find the missing stickers?

puppy

duckling

caterpillar

foal

kittens

Can you find
two balls?

owl chick

Follow the lines

First find the stickers to identify the animals, then trace the dotted lines between them.

lion cub

lion

kitten

cat

chick

hen

puppy

dog

Match & color

Find the stickers then color the pictures to match.

giraffe

caterpillar

piglet

Name that animal

Trace over the letters to complete the baby animal names.

kitten

tiger cub

duckling

joey

Color in

Look at the picture then color in the drawing.

foal

bear cub

What's different?

Circle six differences between these two pictures.

Matching pairs

Find the missing stickers then draw a line to the matching baby animals.

Word search

Find the missing stickers then circle the hidden words in the box.

chick   fawn   lamb   kid   foal

a	i	s	m	g	x	r	i	c	p
e	o	f	c	n	d	o	x	u	k
r	d	t	j	c	e	f	a	s	i
f	a	w	n	l	c	t	w	x	d
n	m	i	u	d	f	o	a	l	b
j	k	f	r	i	n	a	p	a	e
e	c	h	i	c	k	n	t	m	x
u	a	r	o	n	f	c	i	b	r

Jigsaw mums

Find the missing jigsaw pieces to complete your favorite animal families.

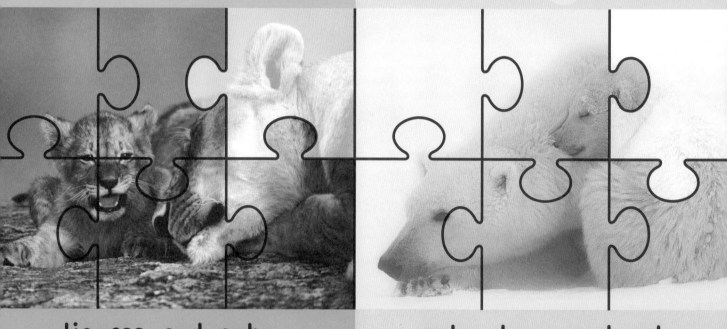

lioness and cub

polar bear and cub

rhinoceros and calf

orangutan and infant

Animal families

Baby animals are not always called the same name as their parents. Can you find the missing stickers?

dog and puppy

Adding

Do each sum, then find the correct sticker to answer each one.

 +  =

1 puppy + 1 puppy is added = How many puppies altogether?

 +  =

1 chick + 2 chicks are added = How many chicks altogether?

 +  =

1 kid + 3 kids are added = How many kids altogether?

Subtracting

Do each sum, then find the correct sticker to answer each one.

 −

4 panda cubs

1 cub is taken away

How many cubs remain?

  =

3 lion cubs

1 cub is taken away

How many cubs remain?

  =

2 kittens

1 kitten is taken away

How many kittens remain?

Hungry maze

Help each baby animal find its favorite food.

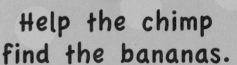

Help the chimp find the bananas.

cheese

dog biscuits

bananas

Help the mouse find the cheese.

Help the puppy find the dog biscuits.

Baby phonics

What kind of animals are these babies? Fill in the missing letters.

_ats

_ats

_og

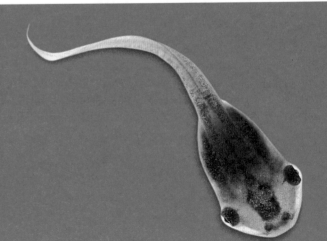

_rog

Caterpillar trail

Which path leads the caterpillar to the leaf?

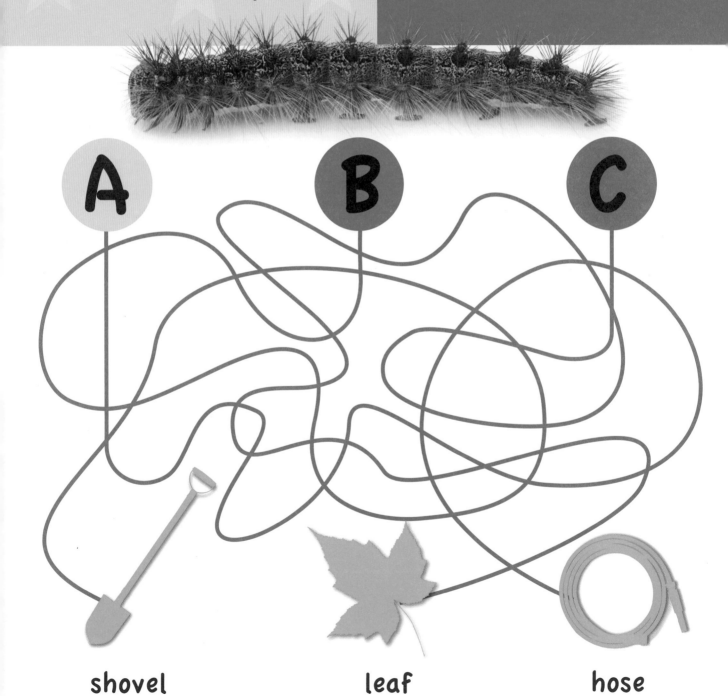

shovel   leaf   hose

Body names

Trace over the letters of these baby animal body names.

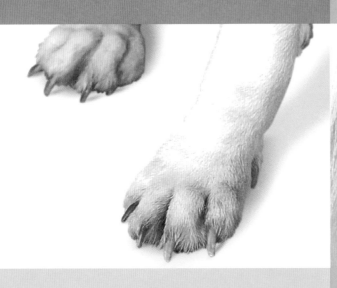

paws

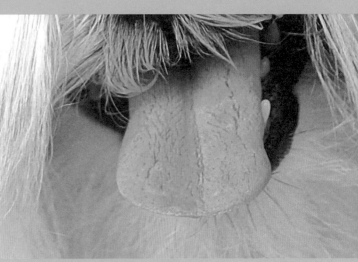

tongue

shell

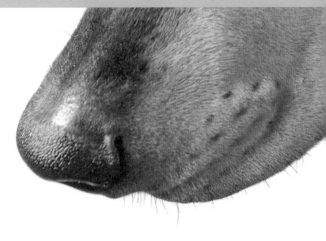

snout

Dot to dot

Starting at number 1 join the dots to complete each animal picture.

elephant calf

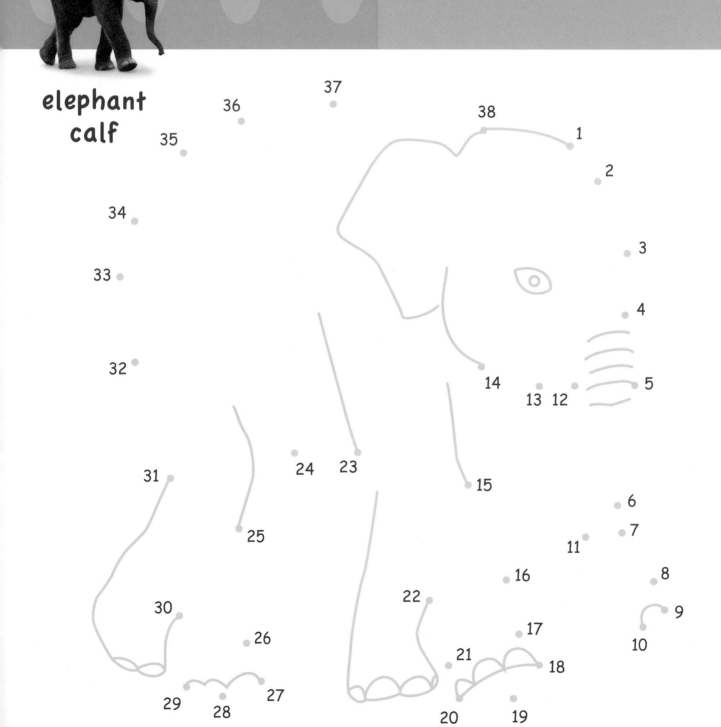

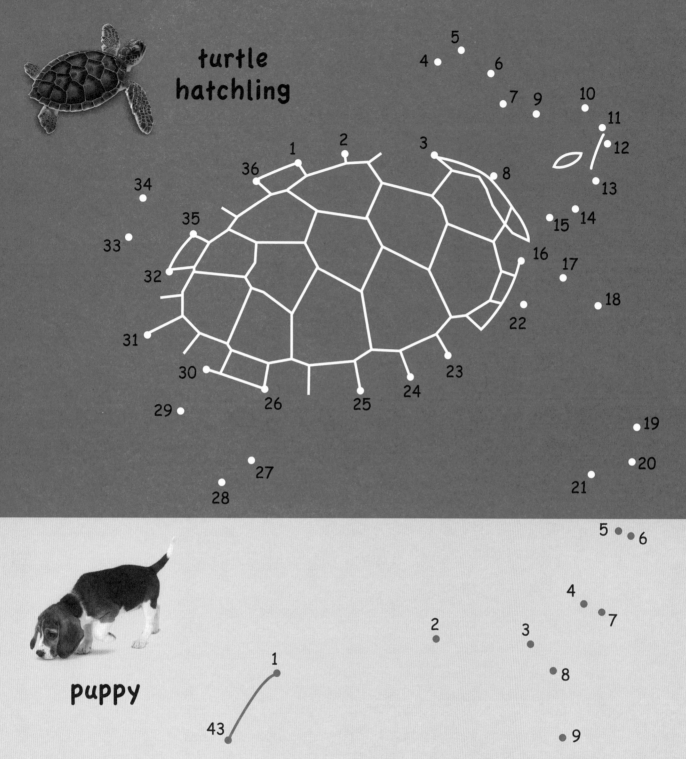

turtle hatchling

puppy

Follow the lines

First find the stickers to identify the animals then trace the dotted lines between them.

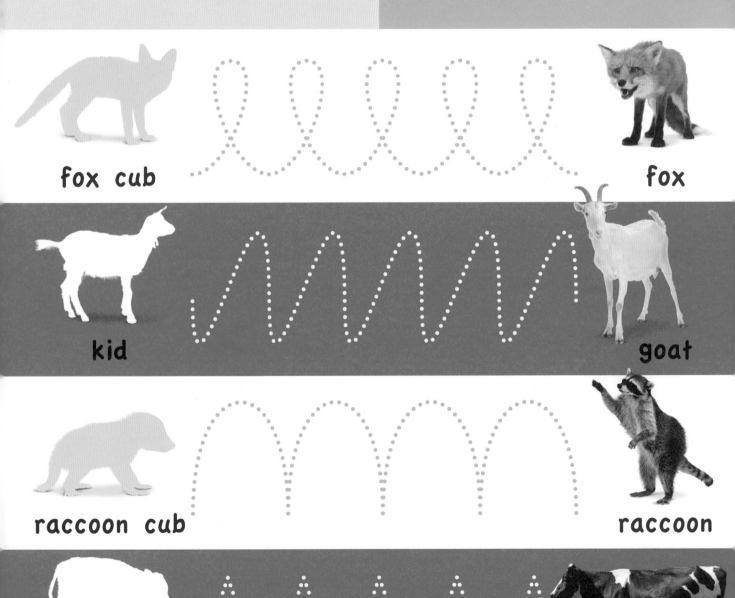

fox cub

fox

kid

goat

raccoon cub

raccoon

calf

cow

Woolly maze

Help the lamb find her mother.

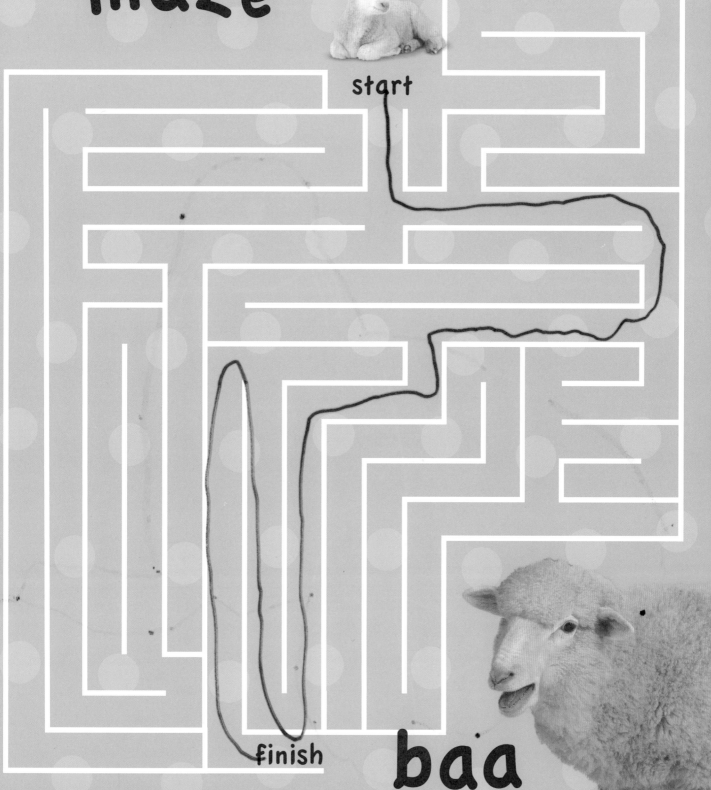

start

finish

baa

Dot to dot

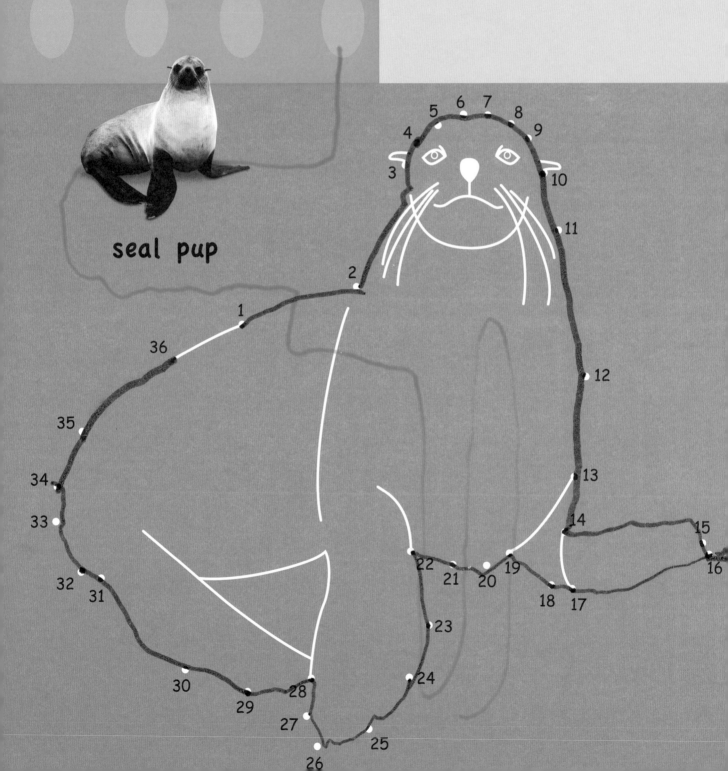

seal pup

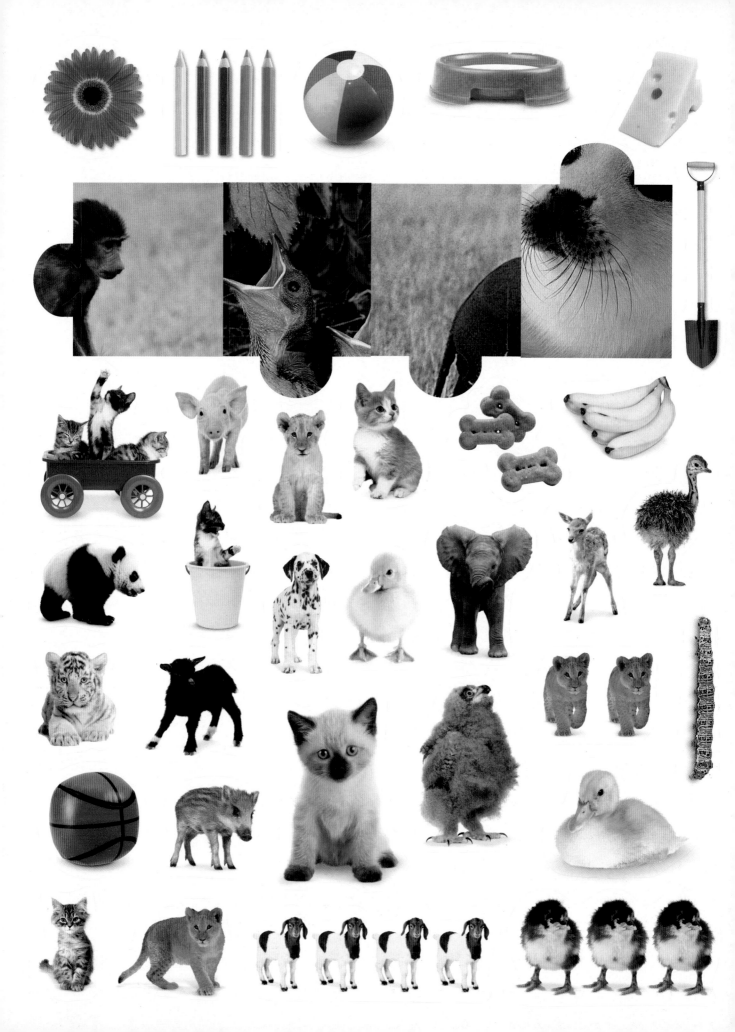

Farm Animals

On the farm

Many things go on at the farm. Can you find the missing stickers?

barn

turkey

Can you find four sunflowers?

Silos store grain.

crows

tractor

cows

scarecrow

hen and chicks

Animal snap

Find the missing numbers to complete the cards. Then you and a friend can play a game. Point to a card, then find another that is exactly the same.

10

7

2

3

8

4

6

9

5

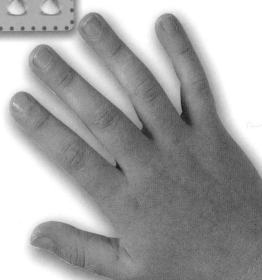

10

1

8

Name that animal

Trace over the letters to complete the animal names.

turkey

pig

rabbit

sheep

Jigsaw faces

Find the missing jigsaw pieces to complete your favorite farm animals.

rooster

sheep

horse

cow

Match making

Animals produce many foods and fabrics such as wool. Find the missing stickers then draw a line connecting each pair

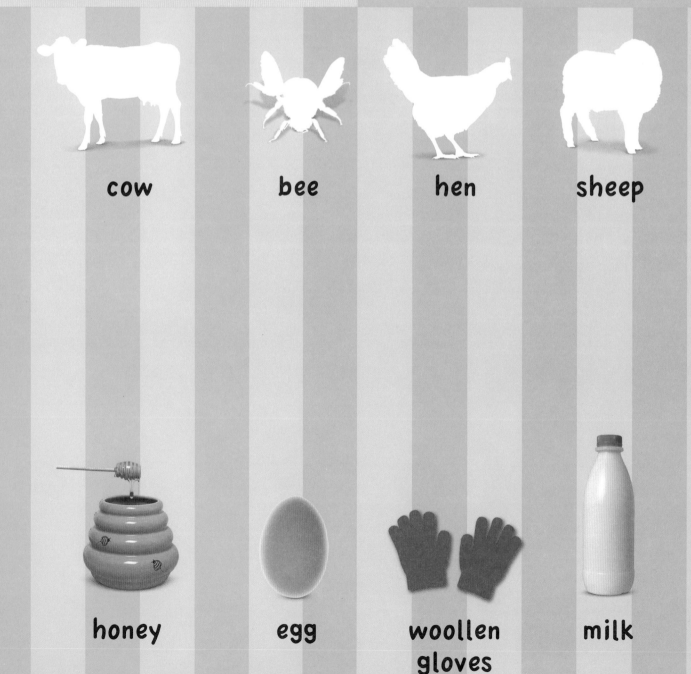

cow

bee

hen

sheep

honey

egg

woollen gloves

milk

What's different?

Circle seven differences between these two pictures.

Match & color

Find the sticker then color in the drawing to match.

rooster

Word search

Find the missing stickers then circle the hidden words in the box.

duck

donkey

turkey

goose

sheep

x	a	u	i	m	z	p	a	s	t
h	i	d	o	n	k	e	y	f	l
n	t	u	r	k	e	y	s	d	k
a	i	c	b	u	a	e	h	o	t
h	q	k	w	i	a	k	e	r	z
b	a	t	g	o	o	s	e	h	m
y	h	i	c	n	r	k	p	c	e
a	w	f	o	c	h	r	j	e	i

Rabbit trail

Which path leads the rabbit to the carrots?

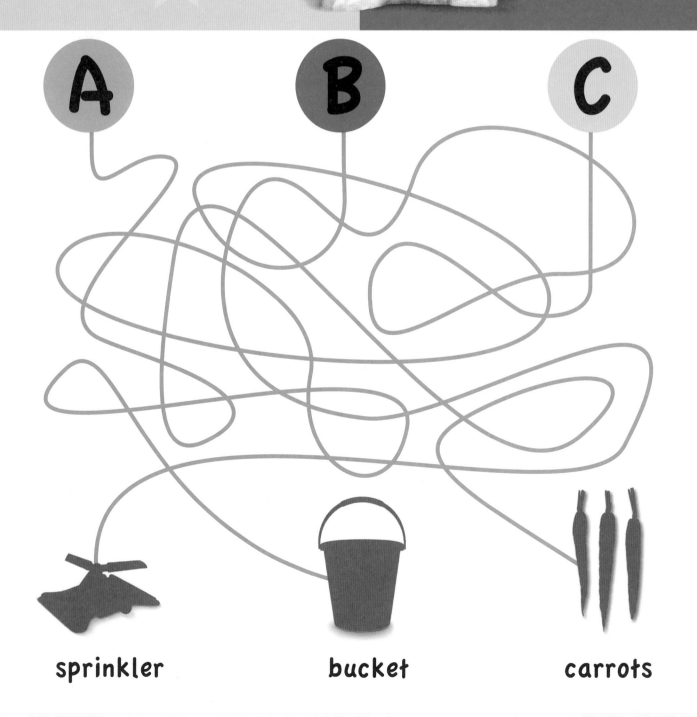

A

B

C

sprinkler

bucket

carrots

farm patterns

Find the missing stickers to complete the patterns.

counting animals

Count the farm animals then find the matching sticker and correct number.

1	2	3	4
lamb	pig	turkey	duckling

follow the lines

First find the stickers to identify the animals then trace the dotted lines.

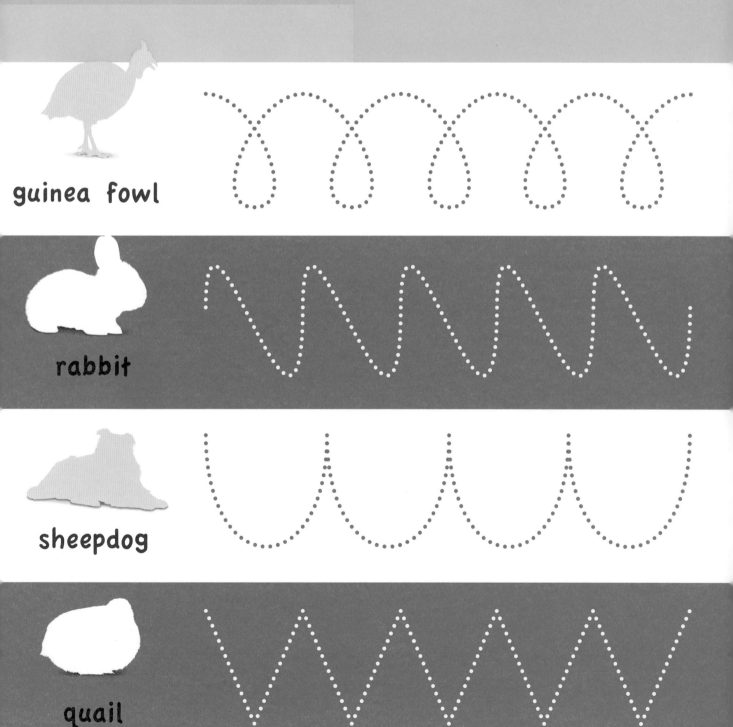

guinea fowl

rabbit

sheepdog

quail

Animal sounds

Animals make many different sounds. Can you find the missing stickers?

calf

cock-a doodle-doo

rooster

turkey

Farm phonics

Fill in the letters that make the short vowel sounds.

p_g

d_ck

h_n

d_g

Color in

Look at the picture then color in the drawing.

duck

turkey

What's different?

Circle six differences between these two pictures.

Matching pairs

Find the missing stickers then draw a line to the matching farm animals.

Match & color

Find the sticker then color in the drawing to match.

pig

Body names

feet

horn

ears

snout

Dot to dot

Starting at number 1 join the dots to complete the animal picture.

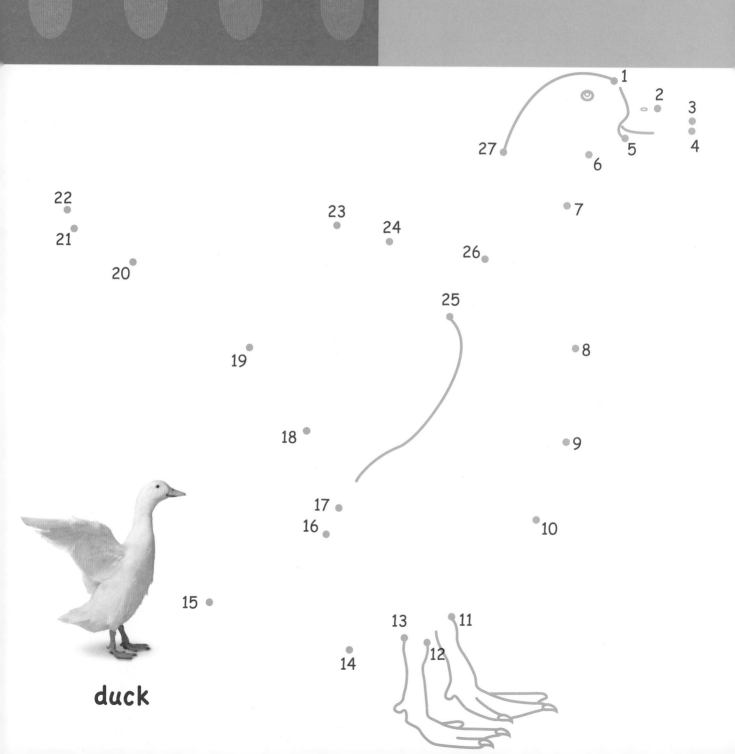

1

2

3

4

5

6

27

7

22

21

23

24

26

20

25

19

8

18

9

17

16

10

25

15

13 11

12

14

duck

Round up maze

Help the sheepdog round up the lambs.

sheepdog

start

finish

lambs

Word search

Find the missing stickers then circle the hidden words in the box.

llama   horse   mice   guinea pig   rabbit

a	s	t	d	j	l	l	a	m	a
f	x	m	r	b	r	z	k	e	l
g	u	i	n	e	a	p	i	g	d
r	n	c	v	y	b	k	l	y	q
p	o	e	m	n	b	u	p	o	s
m	e	h	y	t	i	o	r	a	t
u	i	a	r	c	t	b	w	m	j
a	g	h	o	r	s	e	t	i	x

Goat path

Which path leads the goats to the straw bale?

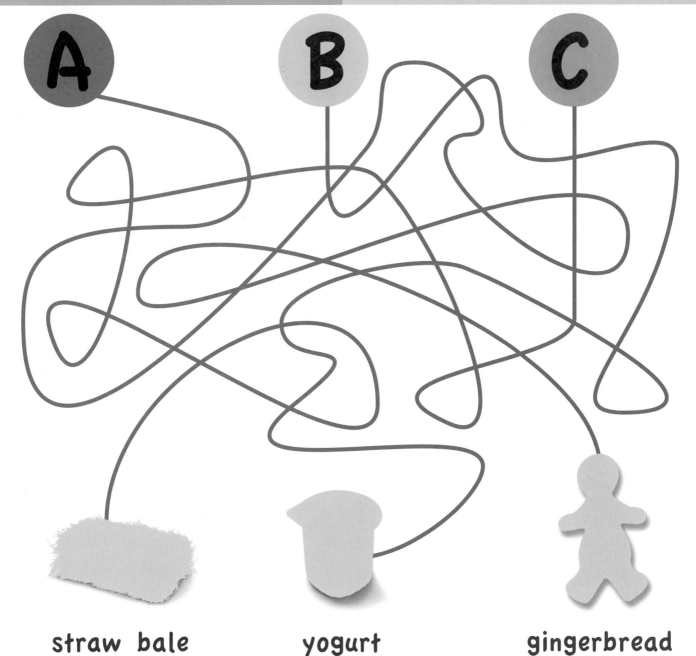

A

B

C

straw bale   yogurt   gingerbread

Egg mazing

Help the hen find her eggs.

start

finish

Find three eggs.

jigsaw faces

Find the missing jigsaw pieces to complete your favorite farm animals.

ram

donkey

dog

pig

Dot to dot

Starting at number 1 join the dots to complete the animal picture.

rooster

gobble
gobble

ee-aw

baaa

moo

honk

Wild Animals

Animal halves

Find the missing stickers then color the missing half of the animal.

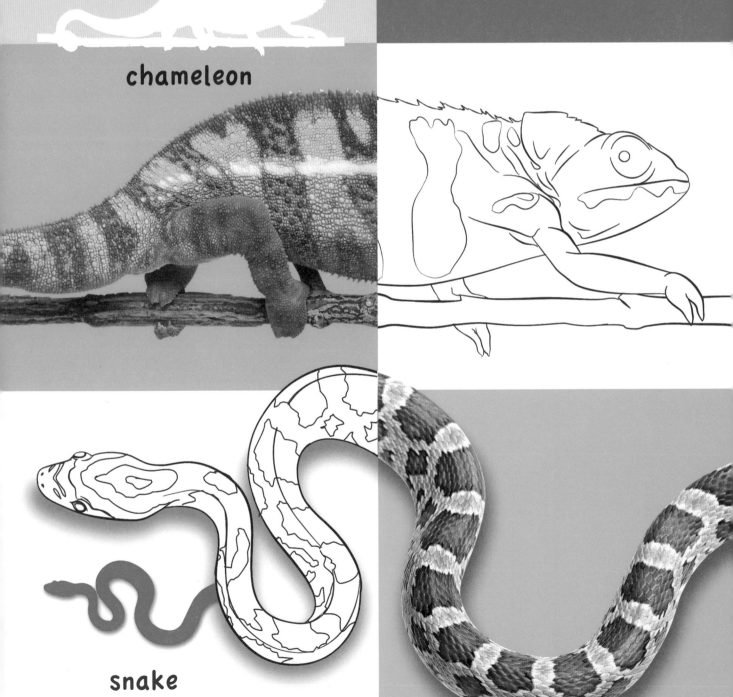

chameleon

snake

Counting animals

Count the wild animals then find the matching sticker and correct number.

1

2

3

4

chimpanzee   cheetah   cockatoo   emu

Animal patterns

Wild animals have many interesting patterns. Can you find the missing stickers?

python

butterfly

zebra

tiger

elephant

giraffe

leopard

peacock

turtle

Wild phonics

Fill in the letters that make the missing vowel sounds.

t_ger

p_ma

sn_ke

_mu

Animal homes

Find the missing animals then draw a line to their homes.

polar bear   camel   koala   clown fish

coral reef   forest   Arctic   desert

Match & color

Find the sticker then color in the drawing to match.

mandrill

Word search

Find the missing stickers then circle the hidden words in the box.

| elephant | wolf | zebra | lizard | puffin |

e	a	s	u	i	z	h	p	s	c
o	l	v	h	k	e	d	o	m	x
f	w	b	n	e	b	a	t	c	p
z	o	b	a	g	r	u	i	a	u
e	l	e	p	h	a	n	t	y	f
o	f	m	n	u	e	t	o	k	f
m	a	o	l	i	z	a	r	d	i
k	g	i	a	s	y	o	p	x	n

Counting animals

How many lizards are there? 1

How many snails are there? 2

How many ladybugs are there? 3

How many butterflies are there? 4

How many ants are there? 5

Matching pairs

Find the missing stickers then draw a line to the matching wild animals.

Body names

Trace over the letters to complete the wild animal body names.

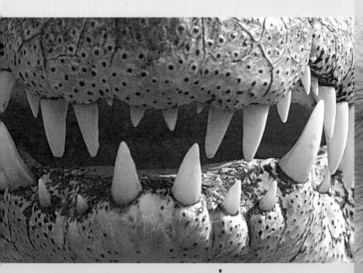

teeth

eyes

nose

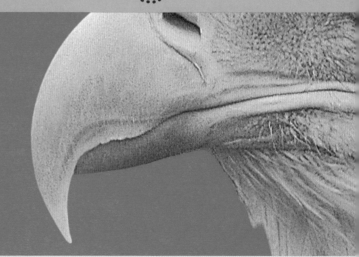

beak

Eagle trail

Which path leads the bald eagle to the fish?

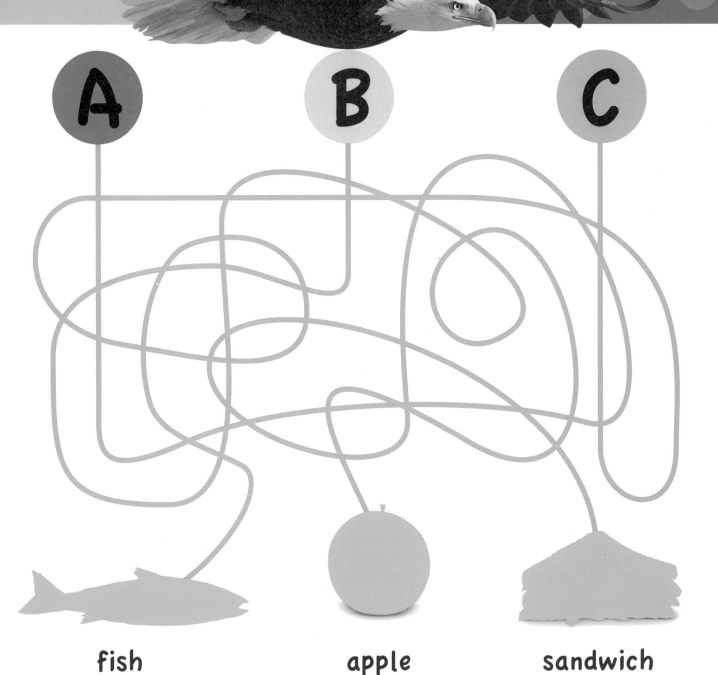

A

B

C

fish

apple

sandwich

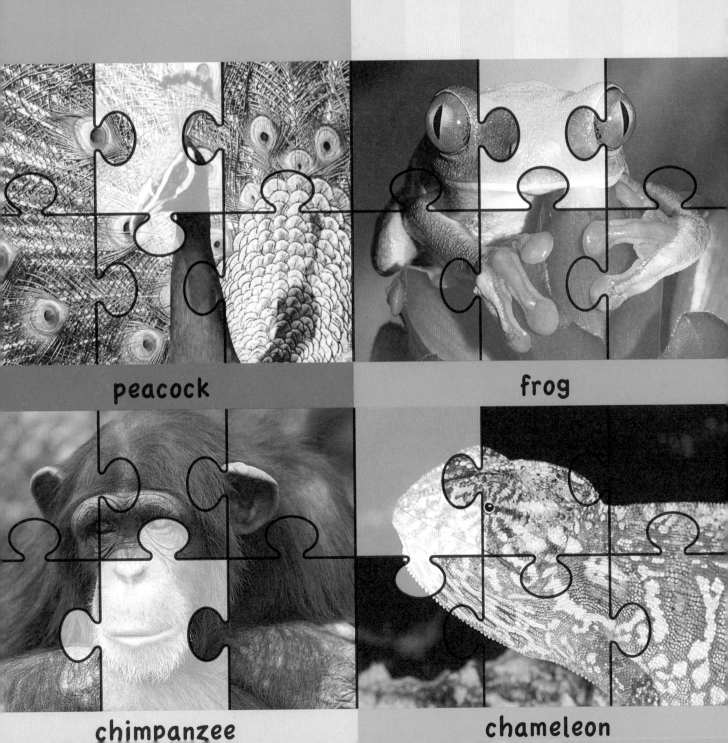

Jigsaw faces

Find the missing jigsaw pieces to complete your favorite wild animals.

peacock

frog

chimpanzee

chameleon

Wild patterns

Find the missing stickers to complete the patterns.

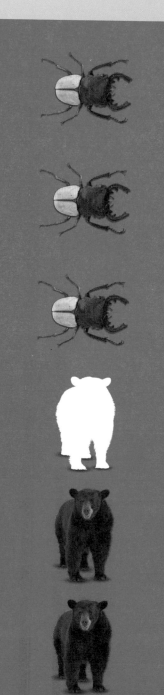

Wild colors

Wild animals come in many colors. Can you complete the picture?

Animal colors

Trace over the letters to complete the animal colors.

red

blue

yellow

black

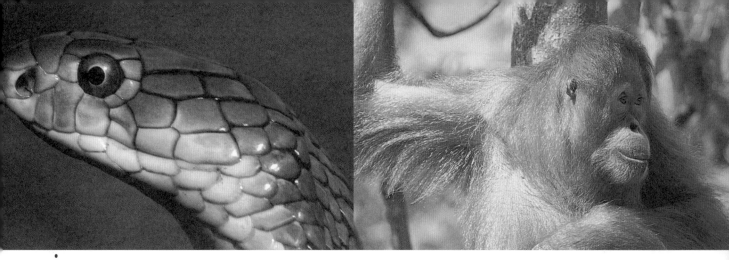

brown orange

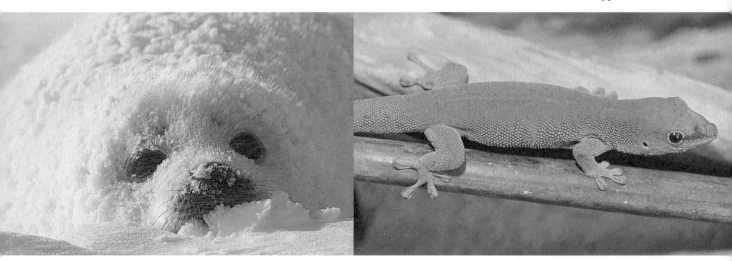

white green

pink gray

jigsaw mouths

Find the missing jigsaw pieces to complete your favorite wild animals.

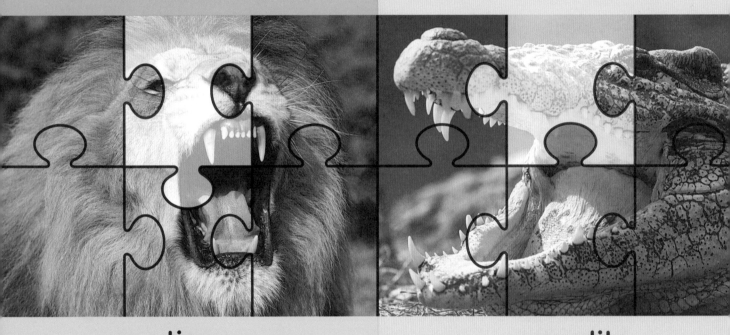

lion

crocodile

hippopotamus

eagle

squirrel fun

Which path leads the squirrel to the hazelnuts?

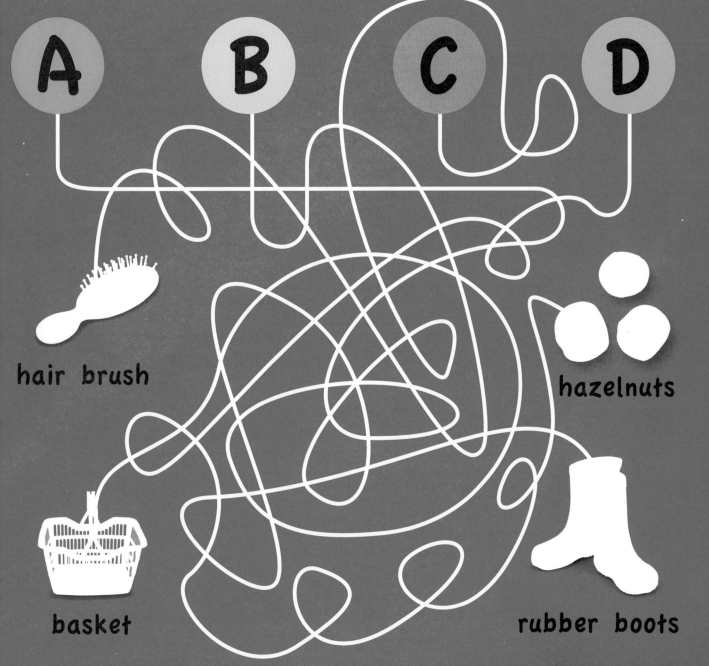

A **B** **C** **D**

hair brush

hazelnuts

basket

rubber boots

What's different?

Circle five differences between these two pictures.

follow the lines

First find the stickers to identify the animals then trace the dotted lines.

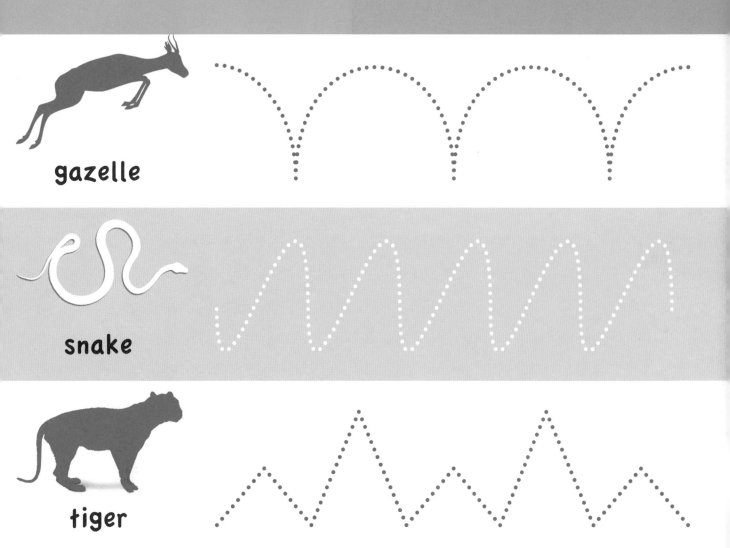

gazelle

snake

tiger

armadillo

Word search

Find the missing stickers then circle the hidden words in the box.

ocelot   porcupine   giraffe   jaguar   deer

r	d	s	u	i	m	o	g	k	c
h	n	e	o	a	v	m	f	d	e
p	o	r	c	u	p	i	n	e	m
r	a	n	e	t	s	b	r	e	c
o	g	j	l	w	n	i	a	r	p
h	s	a	o	j	a	g	u	a	r
r	a	s	t	i	o	s	t	u	c
o	t	g	i	r	a	f	f	e	x

Grassy maze

Help the elephant calf find the grass.

elephant calf

start

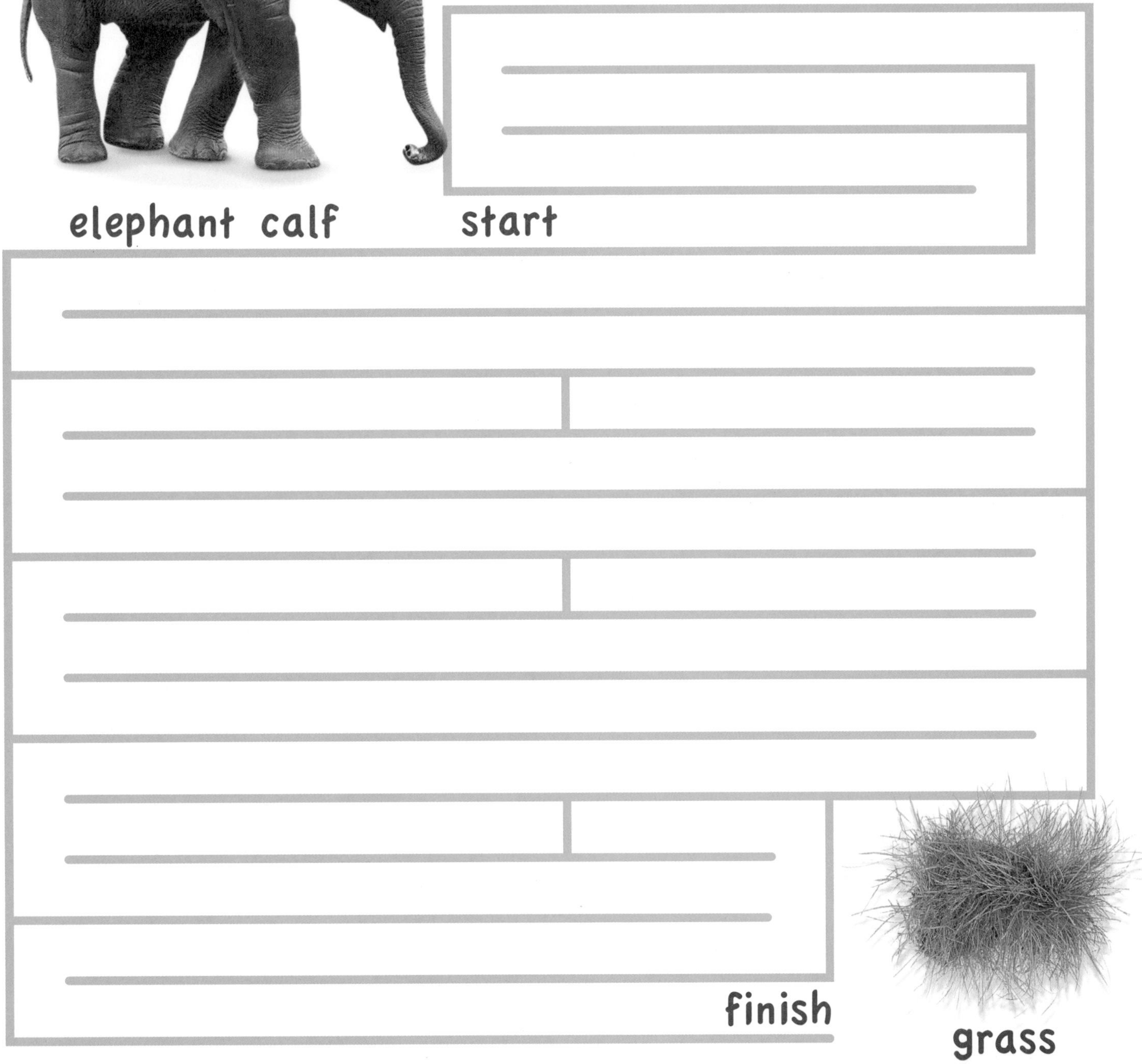

finish

grass

Dot to dot

Starting at number 1 join the dots to complete each animal picture.

hippopotamus

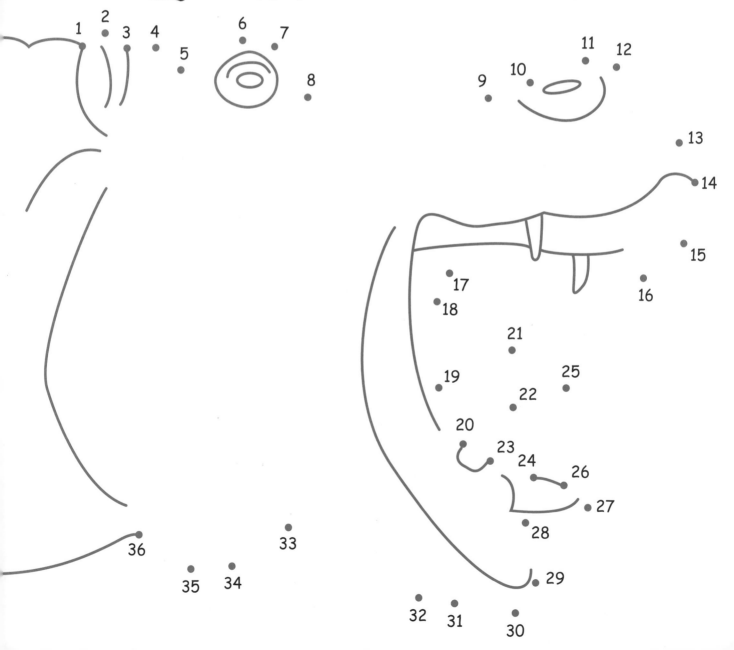

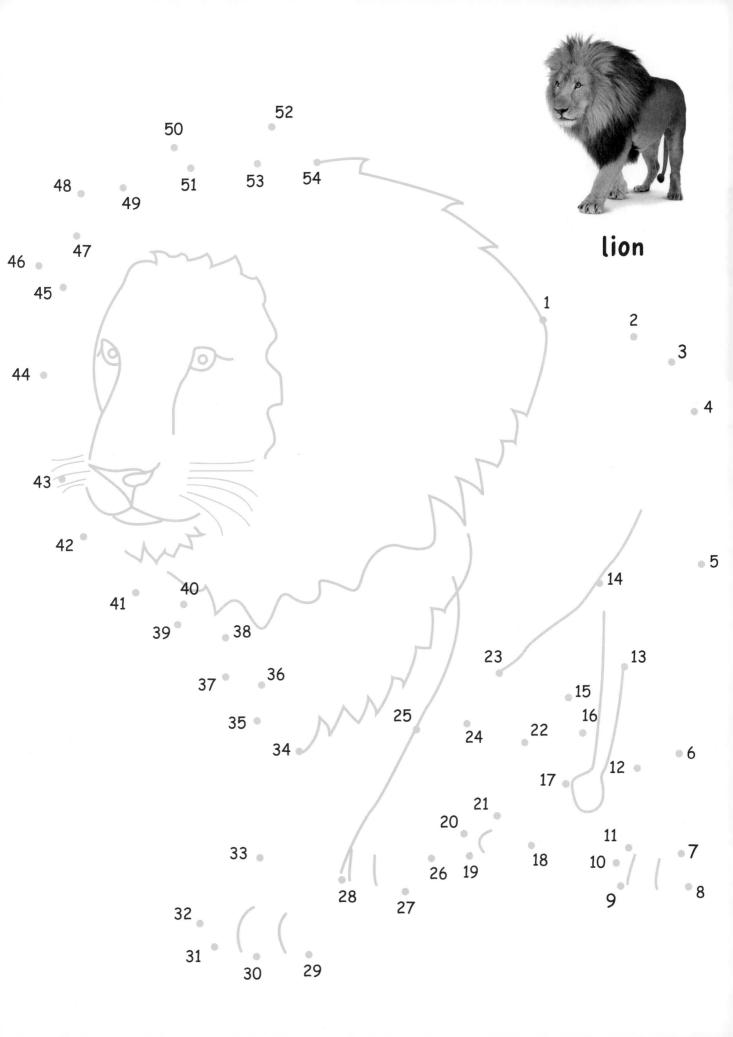

lion

What's different?

Circle seven differences between these two pictures.

Write & color

Trace the letters to complete this animal's name, then color the picture on the right.

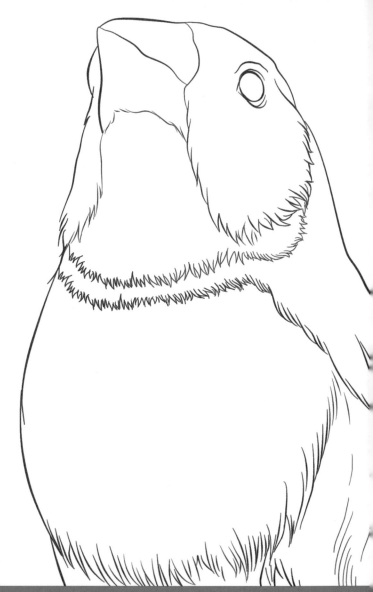

finch

slimy maze

Help the snails find the lettuce.

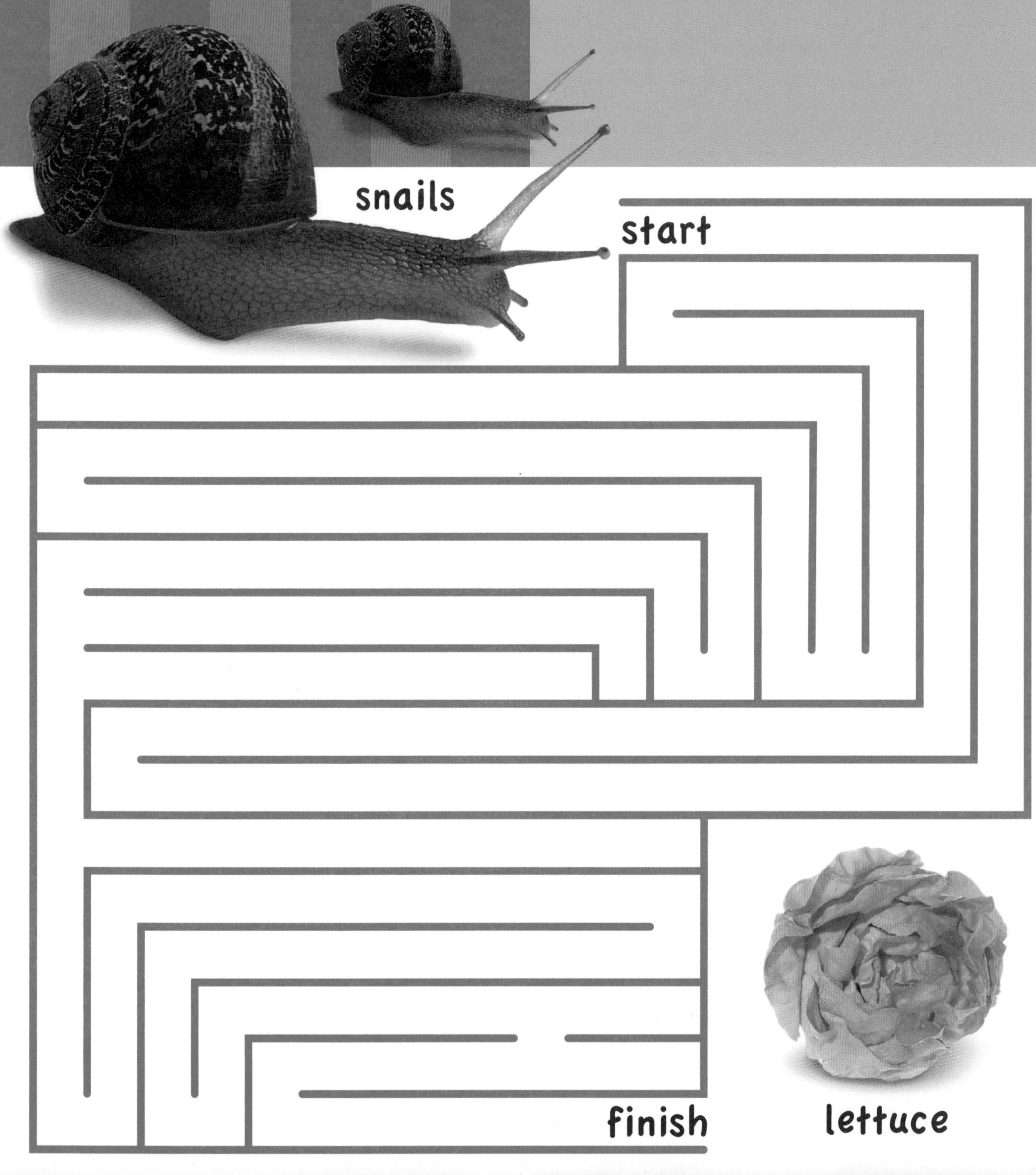

snails

start

finish

lettuce

Dot to dot

Starting at number 1 join the dots to complete each animal picture.

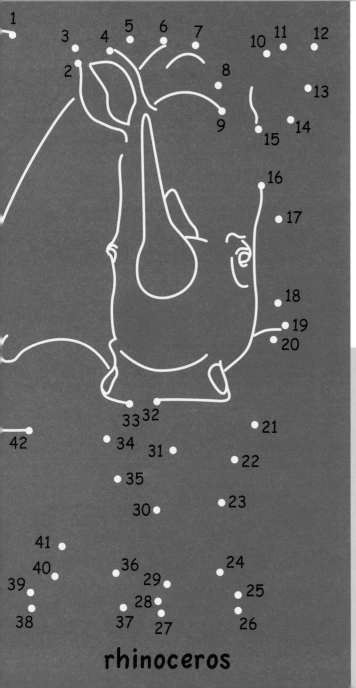

rhinoceros

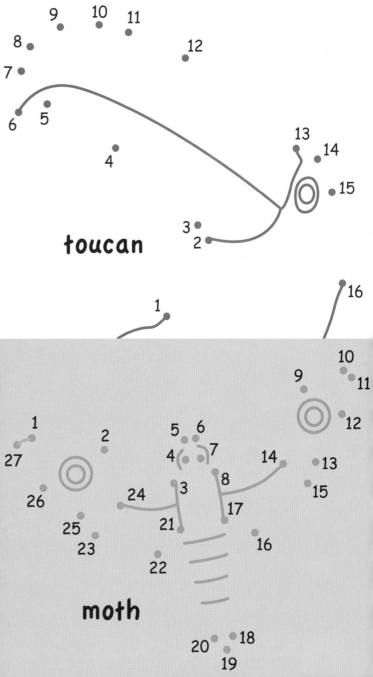

toucan

moth

Animal disguises

Find the missing jigsaw pieces to complete the scenes. Can you see the camouflaged animals?

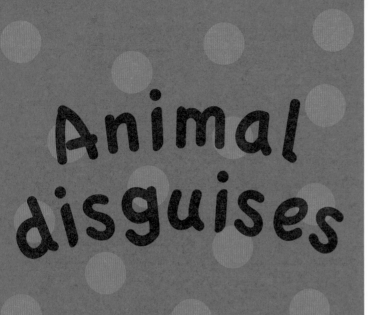

snake

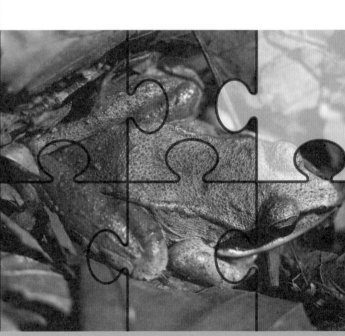

frog

lizard

fish

Water Animals

In the ocean

Many animals live
in the ocean.
Can you find
them all?

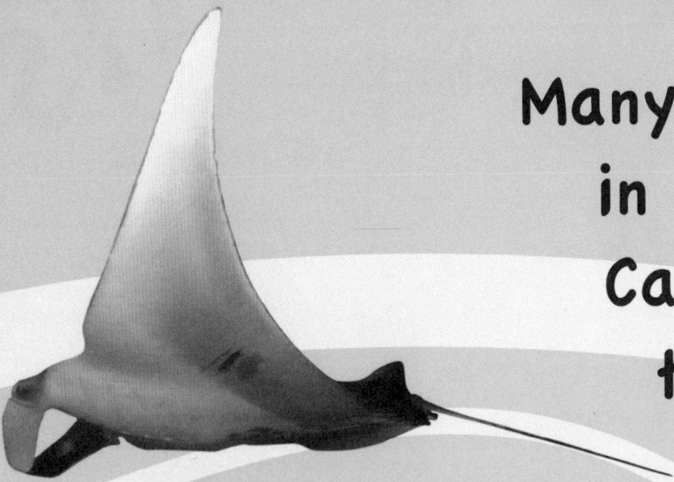

stingray

sea snake

octopus

sea dragon

starfish

shark

damselfish

sea turtle

angel fish

Matching cards

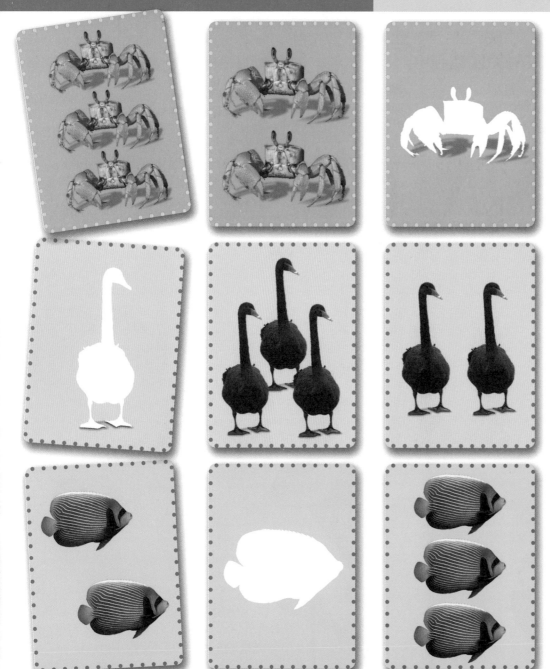
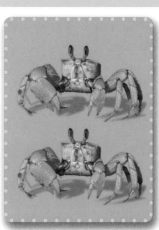

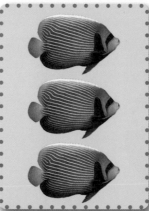

jigsaw faces

Find the missing jigsaw pieces to complete your favorite sea animals.

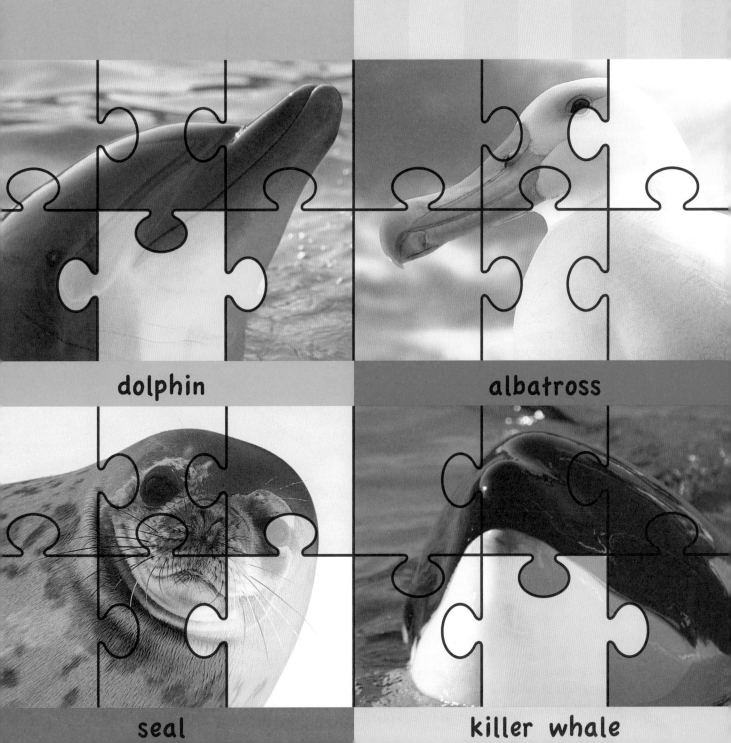

dolphin

albatross

seal

killer whale

Matching pairs

Find the missing stickers then draw a line to the matching water animals.

Animal halves

Find the missing stickers then color the missing half of the animal.

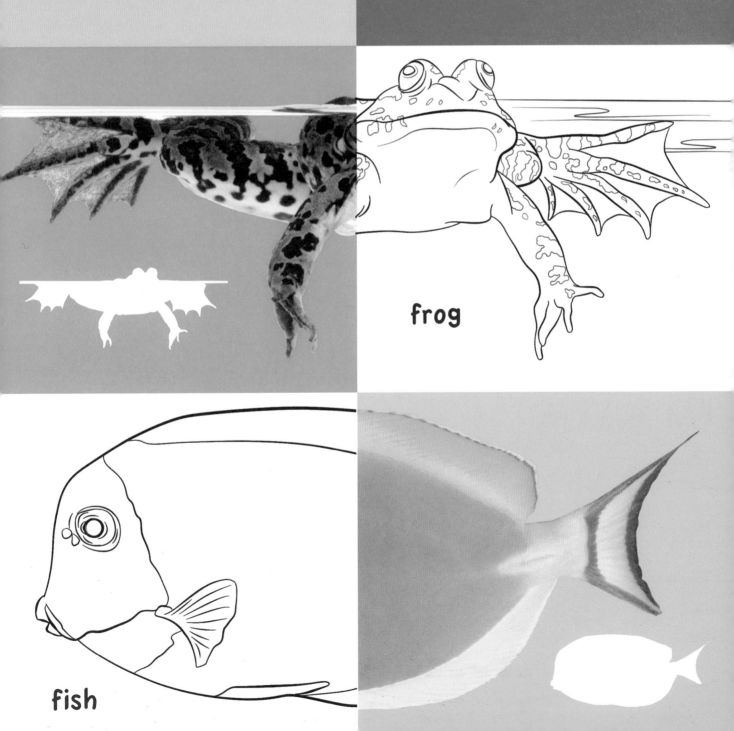

frog

fish

Match & color

Find the sticker then color in the drawing to match.

fish

Word search

Find the missing stickers then circle the hidden words in the box.

penguin   starfish   lobster   dolphin   seal

h	g	u	i	a	s	d	e	a	x
d	c	x	p	e	n	g	u	i	n
o	e	f	b	m	y	a	r	l	q
l	r	o	t	j	k	e	n	w	u
p	d	s	t	a	r	f	i	s	h
h	r	e	h	w	m	o	c	r	a
i	c	a	n	t	o	p	a	f	k
n	r	l	o	b	s	t	e	r	z

Fishy trail

Which path leads the fish to her friends?

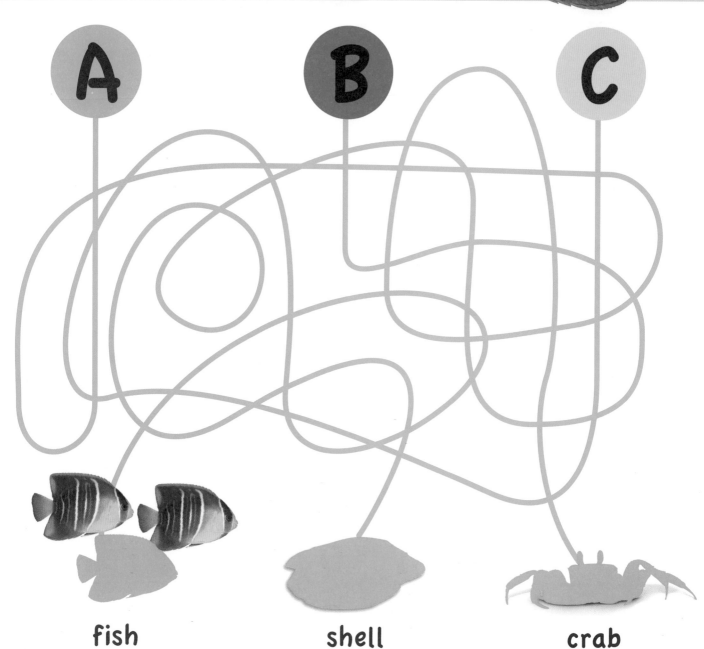

A

B

C

fish

shell

crab

Water phonics

Fill in the letters that make the missing vowel sounds.

wh_le

oct_pus

_el

_onfish

What's different?

Circle seven differences between these two pictures.

Follow the lines

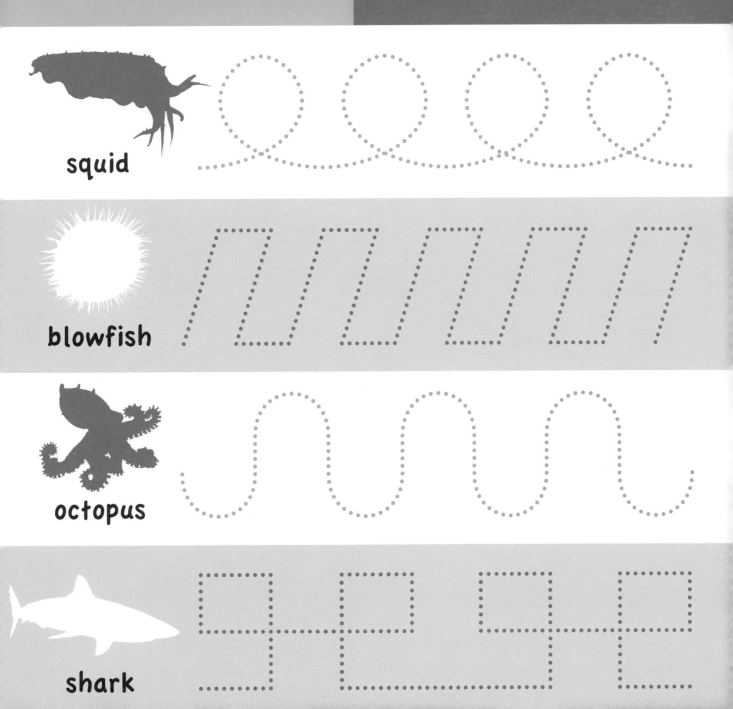

squid

blowfish

octopus

shark

Name that animal

Trace over the letters to complete the water animal names.

shrimp

jellyfish

sea turtle

shark

crab

swan

dolphin

frog

pelican

beaver

Water patterns

Find the missing stickers to complete the patterns.

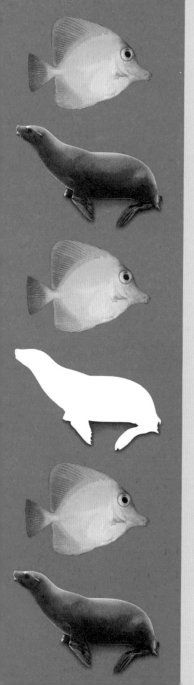

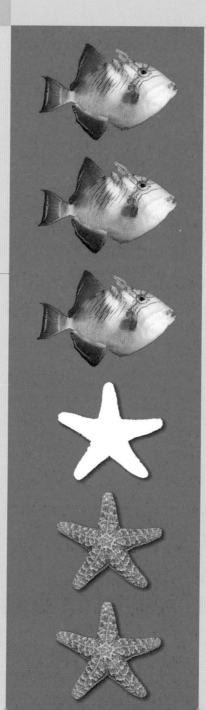

seagull trail

Which path leads the seagulls to the beach?

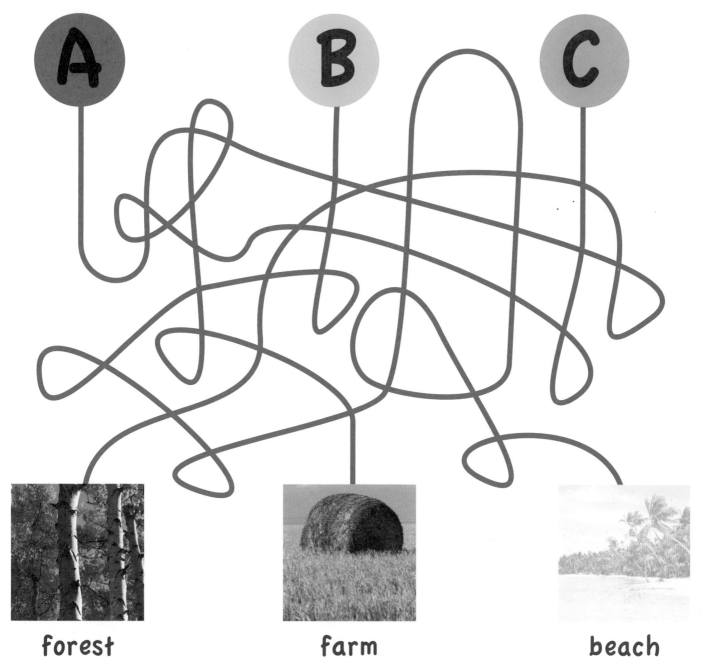

forest

farm

beach

Coral trail

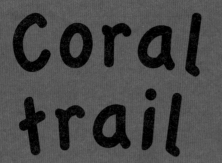

Which path leads the seahorse to the coral?

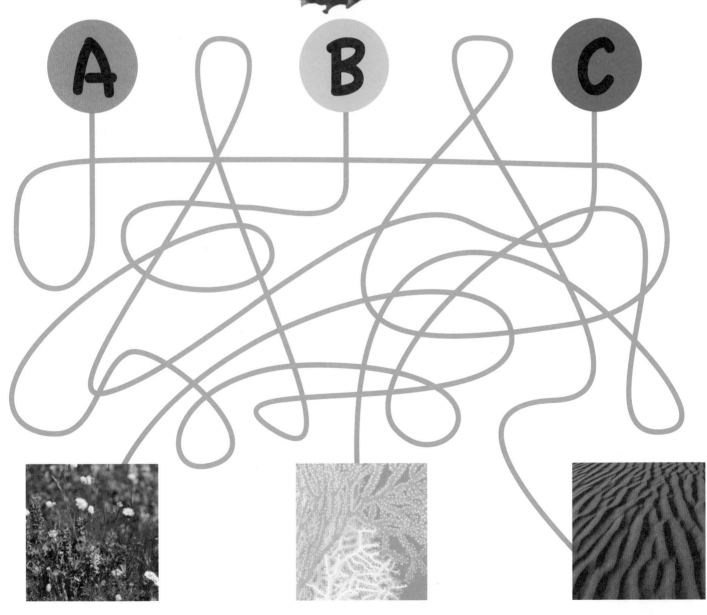

A **B** **C**

meadow coral sand

Body names

Trace over the letters to complete the sea animal body names.

tusks

claw

tail

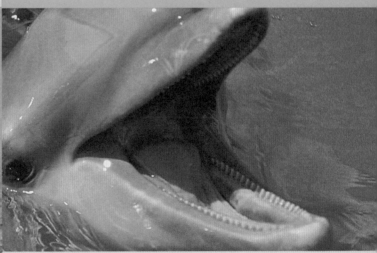

mouth

colorful fish

Fish can be many different shapes and colors. Find the sticker then color in the drawing to match.

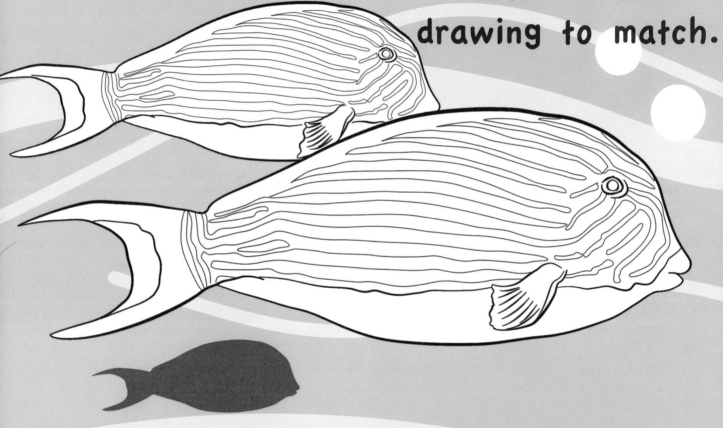

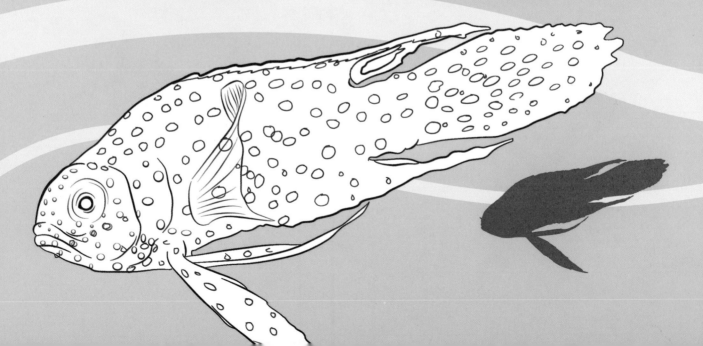

Follow the lines

First find the stickers to identify the animals then trace the dotted lines.

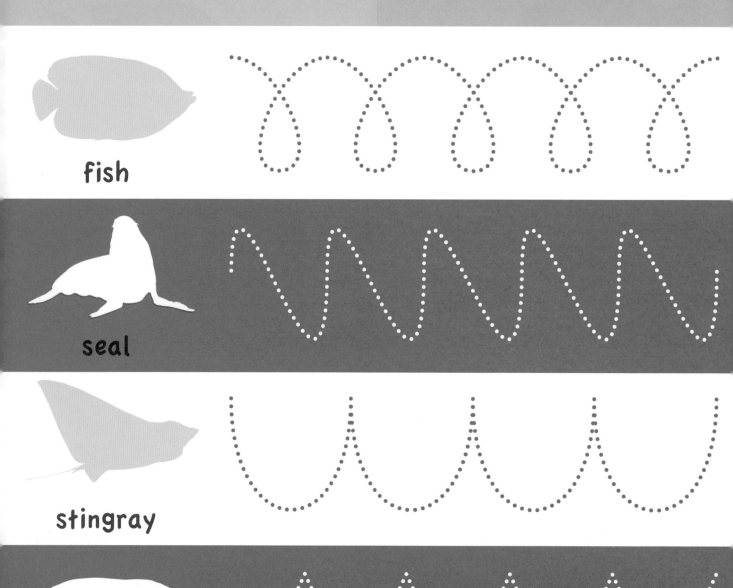

fish

seal

stingray

hippopotamus

Color in

Look at the picture then color in the drawing.

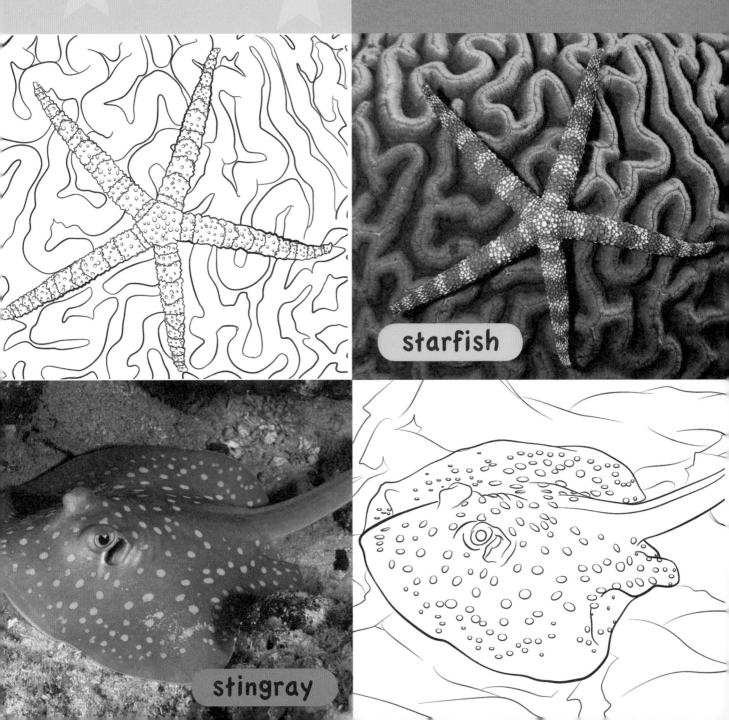

starfish

stingray

Word search

Find the missing stickers then circle the hidden words in the box.

shark   seahorse   crab   crocodile   beaver

x	r	t	c	o	p	a	s	t	f
a	f	n	r	z	c	t	q	b	l
r	s	e	a	h	o	r	s	e	h
a	h	i	b	n	m	t	r	a	u
g	a	u	s	t	r	o	j	v	k
i	r	y	d	w	t	q	d	e	b
o	k	a	t	s	j	u	l	r	x
h	c	r	o	c	o	d	i	l	e

What's different?

Circle six differences between these two pictures.

Write & color

Trace the letters to complete this animal's name, then color the picture on the right.

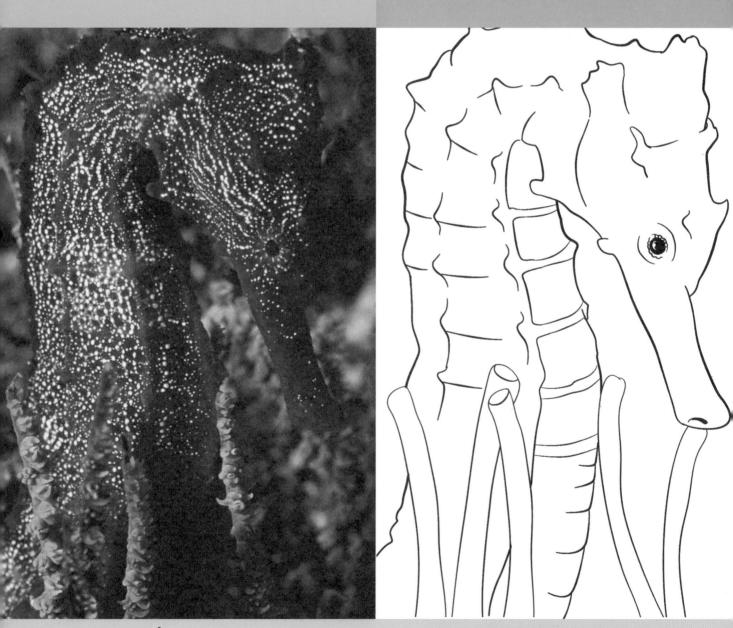

seahorse

polar bear maze

Help the polar bear
find her cubs.

polar bear   start

finish

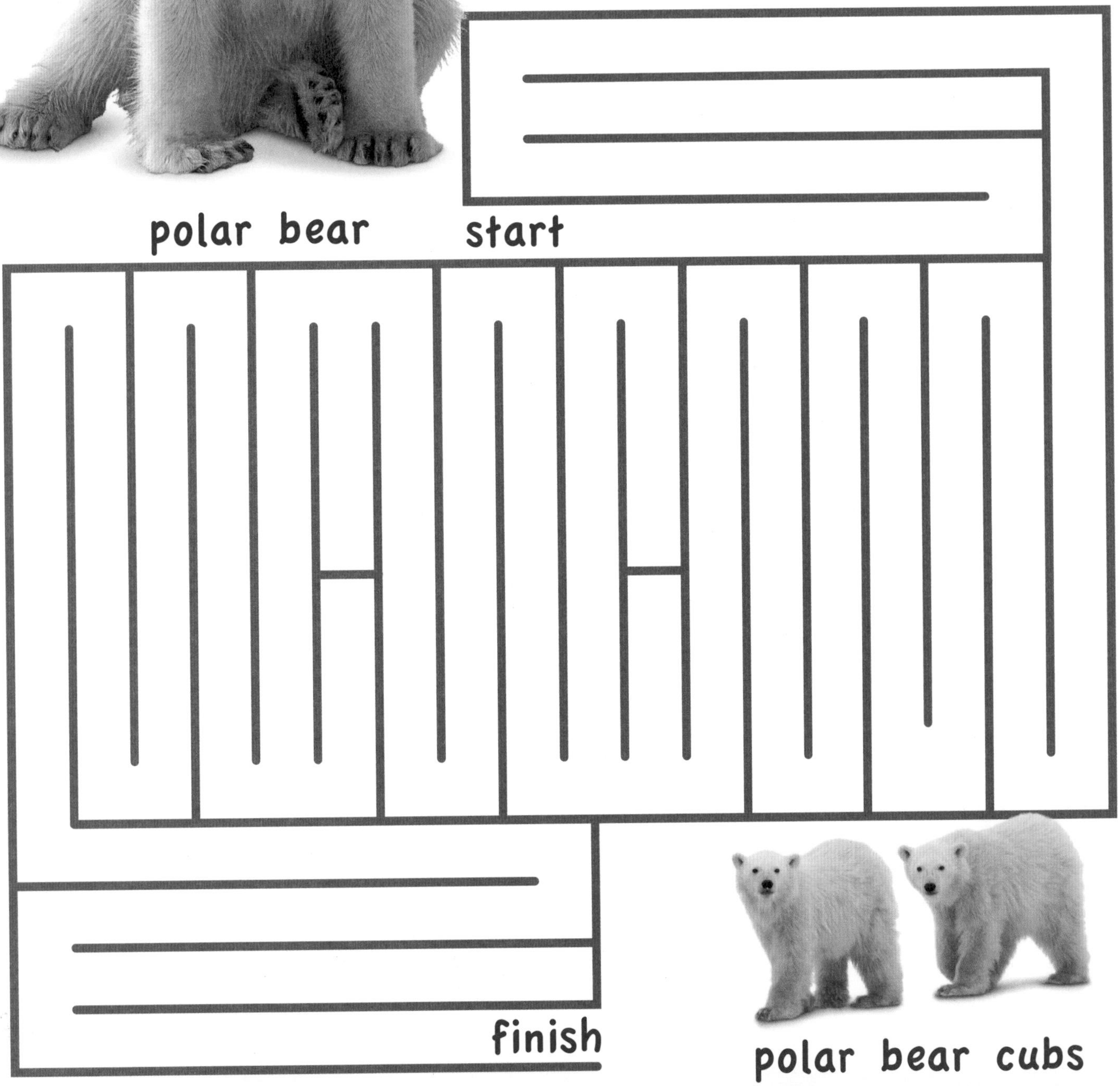

polar bear cubs

Jigsaw faces

Find the missing jigsaw pieces to complete your favorite sea animals.

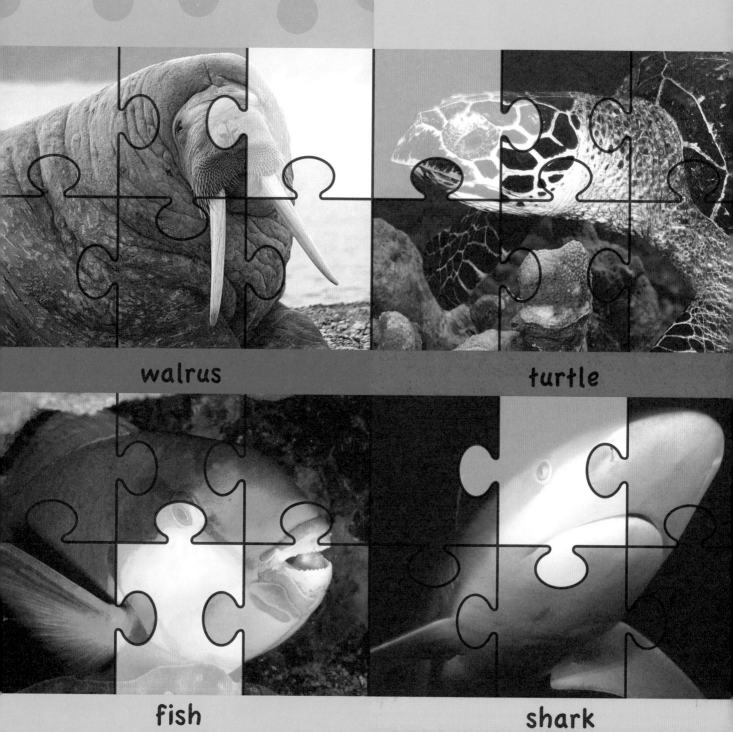

walrus

turtle

fish

shark

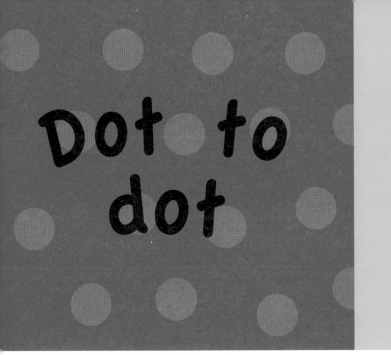

Dot to dot

Starting at number 1 join the dots to complete each animal picture.

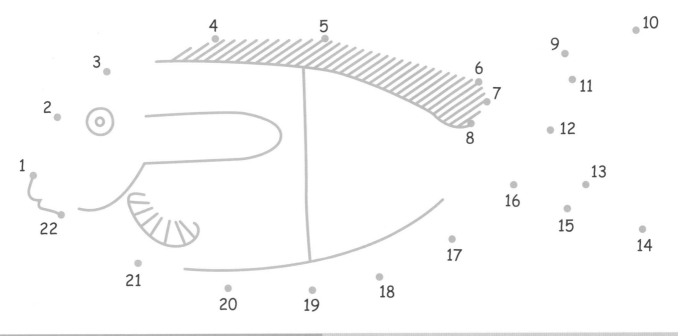

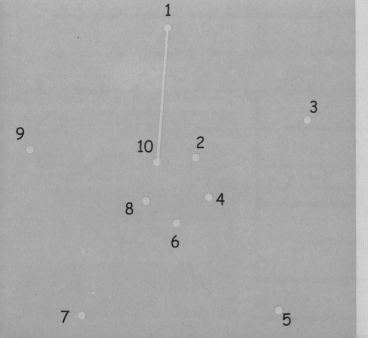

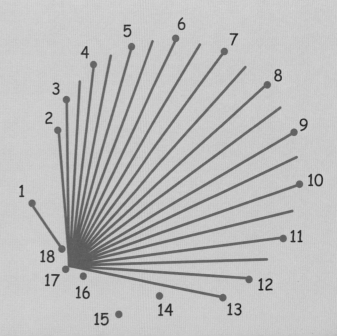

Icy maze

Help the penguins find their way to the ocean.

start

finish

counting animals

Count the water animals and find the matching sticker and correct number.

1 crab

2 swan

3 polar bear

4 fish

Dot to dot

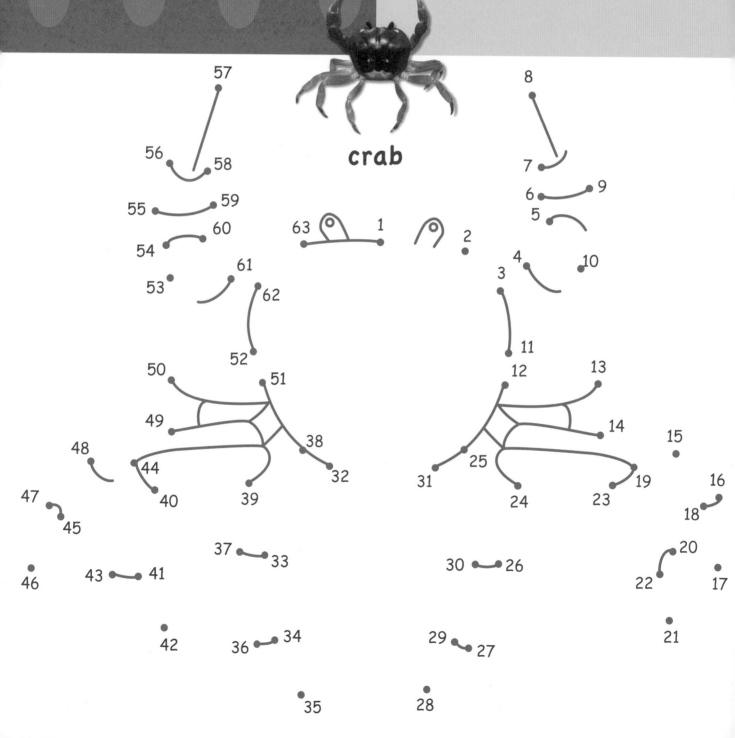

Starting at number 1 join the dots to complete the animal picture.

crab

Bonus stickers